Treasured Story

Read the story, then flip the book over
to complete some underwater activities!

By Barbara Bazaldua
Illustrated by Denise Shimabukuro and Studio IBOIX

First published by Parragon in 2013
Parragon
Chartist House
15-17 Trim Street
Bath BA1 1HA, UK
www.parragon.com

ISBN 978-1-4723-0560-2

Printed in China

Disney
PRINCESS

The Little Mermaid

Bath · New York · Singapore · Hong Kong · Cologne · Delhi
Melbourne · Amsterdam · Johannesburg · Shenzhen

Down in the deepest ocean, there once lived a mermaid princess called Ariel. She was the youngest daughter of King Triton, ruler of the merpeople and she had the most beautiful singing voice in the whole of his kingdom.

Her father loved her dearly, but she was always
getting into trouble.

Ariel longed to be part of the human world and
spent her time exploring old shipwrecks.

When Ariel was sixteen years old, King Triton arranged for her to sing in a magnificent concert and merpeople came from all over the kingdom to hear her. That evening, Ariel was so busy exploring with her friend Flounder that she forgot all about the concert! She had found some human treasures and taken them to the surface to ask Scuttle the seagull what they were.

The Sea King feared for her safety and, thinking humans were dangerous, warned her to stay away from them. But the little mermaid was certain he was wrong. King Triton was furious. "You could have been seen by one of those humans!" he raged. "I'm never to hear of you going to the surface again. Is that clear?" Ariel tried to protest but her father wouldn't listen.

He ordered Sebastian, Ariel's music teacher, to keep an eye on her. But it wasn't an easy task!

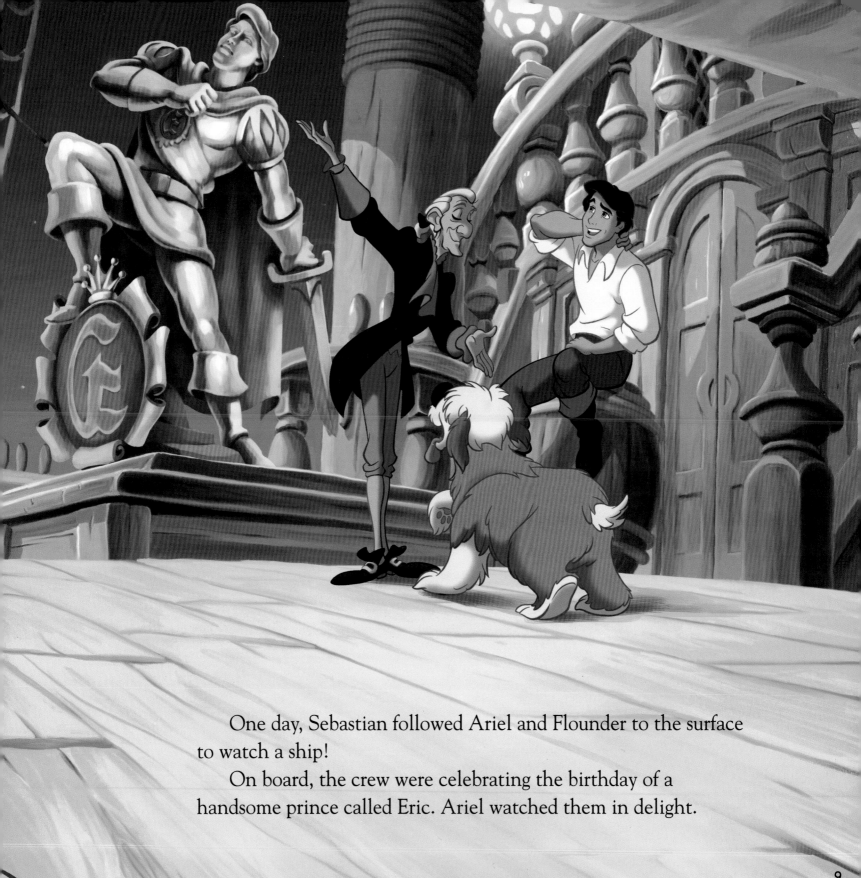

One day, Sebastian followed Ariel and Flounder to the surface to watch a ship!

On board, the crew were celebrating the birthday of a handsome prince called Eric. Ariel watched them in delight.

Soon, storm clouds gathered overhead. Huge waves wrecked the ship and Eric was flung into the sea. Ariel swam quickly to his rescue and pulled him towards the shore.

"Look! He's breathing!" cried Ariel. She gazed at Eric and fell deeply in love. Then, as she sang to him, his eyes began to open. But, hearing a voice in the distance, Ariel slipped back into the water and hid behind a nearby rock. She watched as Eric's servant led him away.

When they were out of sight, Ariel swam home.
"Some day," she vowed to herself, "I'm going to be part
of that human world."

Sebastian had seen everything, and it was not long
before the Sea King learned that Ariel was in love with
a human. Triton was very angry. Determined to teach his
daughter a lesson, he stormed into her secret grotto and
destroyed all her beloved human treasures.

Heartbroken, Ariel sat down and wept. Above her, two sly-looking eels called Flotsam and Jetsam emerged from the shadows. The little mermaid looked up.

"Poor sweet child," they hissed. "Don't be scared. We know someone who can make all your dreams come true. Ursula has great powers."

"The sea witch!" gasped Ariel. She knew that Ursula was her father's worst enemy, who had been banished from his kingdom many years ago and who was now seeking revenge. Ariel hesitated. Then, thinking that it was her only chance to win Prince Eric's love, the little mermaid swam away with the evil eels – quickly followed by Flounder and Sebastian.

Ursula greeted Ariel gleefully. "The only way to get what you want," the sea witch explained, "is to become human yourself. And fortunately I know a little magic."

"Now listen, here's the deal. In exchange for your voice, I will turn you into a human for three days. If Eric hasn't given you the kiss of true love in that time, you will become a mermaid again and belong to me forever." A scroll appeared in Ursula's hand. "Go ahead and sign," she urged.

Ariel was terrified but, thinking of Eric again, she signed. A moment later, she was walking on the seashore – a human at last.

I hereby grant unto URSULA, the Witch of the Sea, one voice, in exchange for byon once high, Dinu gihn thon hteeo serr'n Phur gurrl rekld rdasu retn r m sene urptum srerp monk gueek, Oh trieh nou ri gimn so mund for all eternity. signed,

Prince Eric had been searching everywhere for the girl with the beautiful voice who had rescued him. He had almost given up hope of finding her, when he noticed someone sitting on a rock. This girl looked familiar but, when he found she couldn't speak, Eric realized sadly that she wasn't the one. Feeling sorry for the voiceless girl, he led her back to the palace. And the next day, Eric took Ariel on a tour of his kingdom. They enjoyed being together and Ariel was sure the prince was falling in love with her.

Later that afternoon, when they were boating on a lake, Eric bent forward to kiss Ariel – but at that very moment the boat was overturned.

The sea witch had been watching them and, fearing her plan was about to fail, she sent her precious eels to take action.

Later, disguised as Vanessa, a
beautiful maiden – with Ariel's voice
trapped in a seashell necklace – Ursula
made her way to the shore, where she
captured Prince Eric under her spell.

Eric led Vanessa to the palace and the very next day announced that they were to be married. The wedding ship was to depart at sunset.

Ariel and her friends watched in despair as the sun lowered in the sky.

By chance, Scuttle discovered that Vanessa was really Ursula in disguise and he called on all the sea creatures to stop the wedding. Sebastian went to find the Sea King and Flounder helped Ariel swim towards the wedding ship.

Suddenly, birds swooped down on Vanessa. A lobster pinched her nose and some seals flipped her into the wedding cake! In the chaos, Vanessa's seashell necklace broke and the beautiful voice inside flew back to its rightful owner.

Eric, released from the spell, took Ariel in his arms. Just as he was about to kiss her, the sun sank below the horizon. Straight away, Ariel was turned back into a mermaid. Ursula grabbed her and dived into the water. Her evil cackle echoed eerily around the ship.

"Ursula, stop!" thundered King Triton, rearing up in front of the sea witch. "Let her go!"

"No!" cried Ursula. "She's mine now. You see, we made a deal! However, I might be willing to make an exchange for someone even better," she suggested slyly.

Triton felt he had no choice. He changed the signature on the scroll to his own and handed over his magic trident to the sea witch.

"At last! It's all mine," Ursula screamed. "I am the ruler of the ocean!" Just then, a sharp pain shot through her arm. It was a harpoon thrown by Eric. He had come to rescue Ariel.

The sea witch swelled with anger and towered above them. She summoned the sea's power and stirred up a giant whirlpool, dragging up ancient shipwrecks from the seabed.

Eric scrambled on board one of the decks and, somehow,
he reached the ship's steering wheel. Using all his might, he aimed
the broken bow directly at Ursula. And with a terrible scream she
disappeared under the sea.

Triton's power was instantly restored. He rose to the surface and saw Ariel gazing lovingly at Eric, who was lying on the beach.

"She really does love him," Triton murmured to Sebastian. "I suppose the only problem left is how much I will miss her." Then, with a flourish of his trident, the Sea King granted Ariel her dearest wish – to be human forever. Overjoyed, Eric and Ariel rushed into each other's arms.

A few days later, the couple were married and all their friends were invited to the wedding. King Triton gladly gave Ariel and Eric his blessing, knowing they would live happily ever after.

The End

Now close the book and
flip it over for some
underwater activity fun!

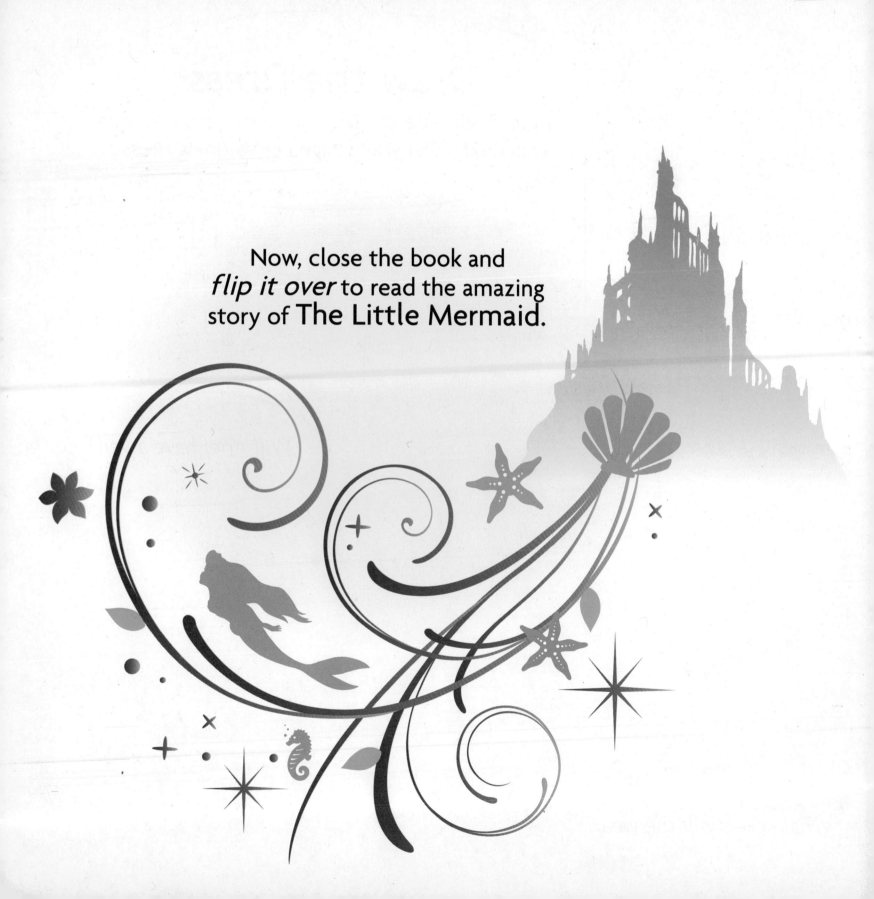

Now, close the book and *flip it over* to read the amazing story of **The Little Mermaid**.

Draw the Dress

Ariel's dreams are coming true and she is marrying Prince Eric. Can you design her wedding dress?

What colour will it be?

Will Ariel have a veil?

What shoes will she wear?

Time to Colour

Ariel and Eric live happily ever after.
Colour in the happy couple and all their friends.

Sudoku

Complete this puzzle by choosing the correct character for each blank square. Each character should appear only once in each box, row and column.

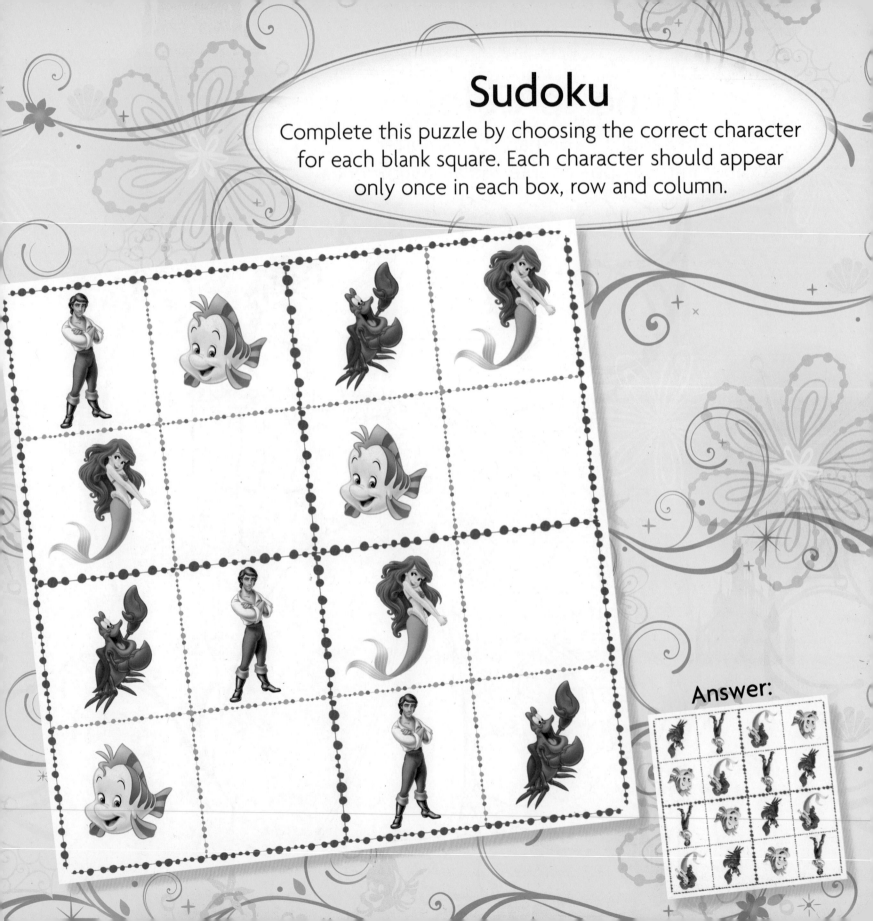

Answer:

Find the Sea Animals

Ariel has lots of friends under the sea and up on the shore. Can you find which characters on this page belong in the sea?

Answers:

The Letter A

Ariel is going to help you learn to write the letter A.
Use the guides to help you write the letter.

A
is for
Ariel

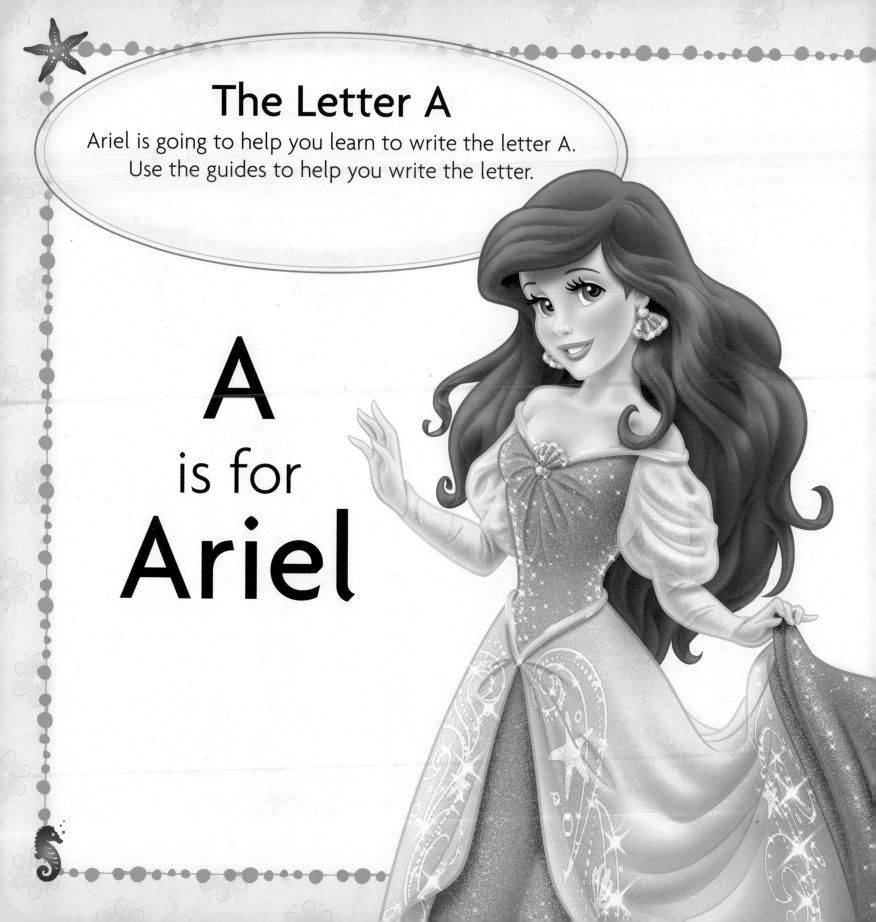

Who Comes Next?

Have a look at the patterns below. Complete them by adding the letter that matches each character.

A   B   C   D

1

2

3

4

Bubble Puzzle

Ariel is ready to say goodbye to her sea friends and go and live as a human with Eric. Can you complete the puzzle by matching the pieces at the bottom of the page to the gaps in this picture?

1 2 3 4 5

The Number 3

Ariel has turned back into a mermaid. She is now back in the sea with her seahorse friends. Learn the number 3 by counting the seahorses and tracing the number.

Time to Colour

After the sea witch gives Ariel legs, Eric finds her washed up on the shore. Colour in Eric and his dog finding the princess.

Time to Colour

Eric and Ariel fall in love under the moonlight.
Colour them in.

To the Prince!

Help Ariel find a way through the maze to Eric.
Watch out for the wicked Ursula along the way.

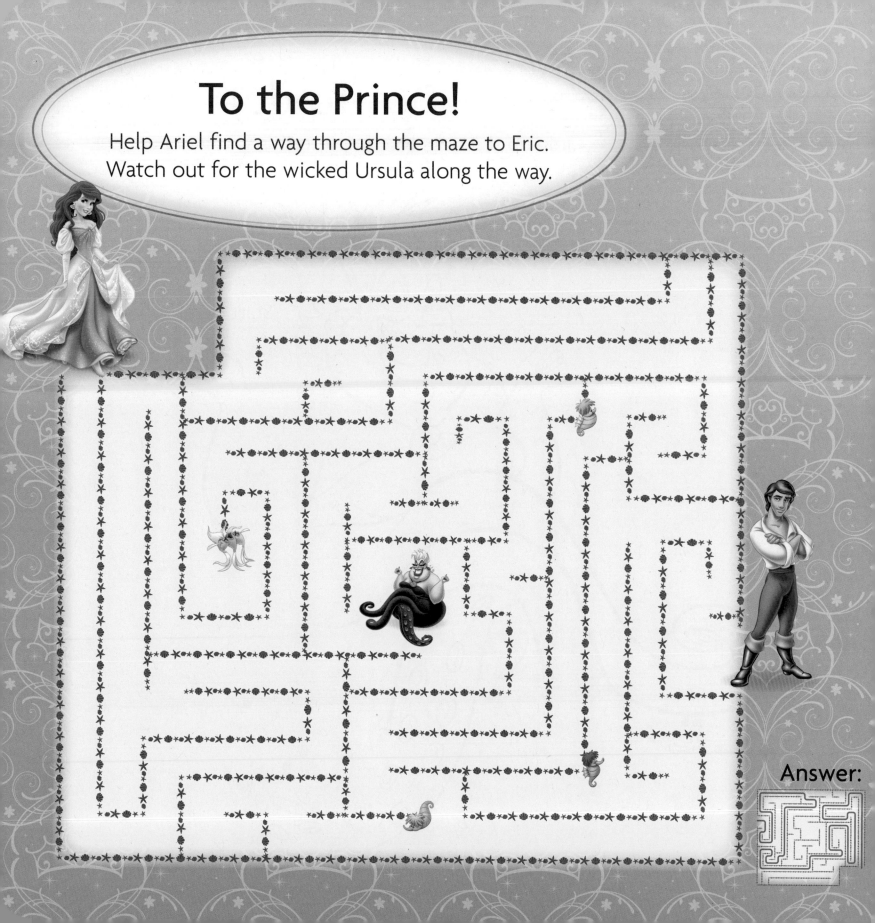

Answer:

Dot-to-dot

Join up the dots to complete this wicked character, then colour her in.

Start Here!

Tangled Lines

King Triton must get to Ariel to save her from the wicked sea witch, Ursula. Which path will take him to his daughter?

1

2

3

Time to Colour

Ariel wishes to be human and to live on the land.
Colour in this dreamer and her friend.

Fish Friends

Life under the sea is full of colourful characters.
Match up each sea creature to the close ups.

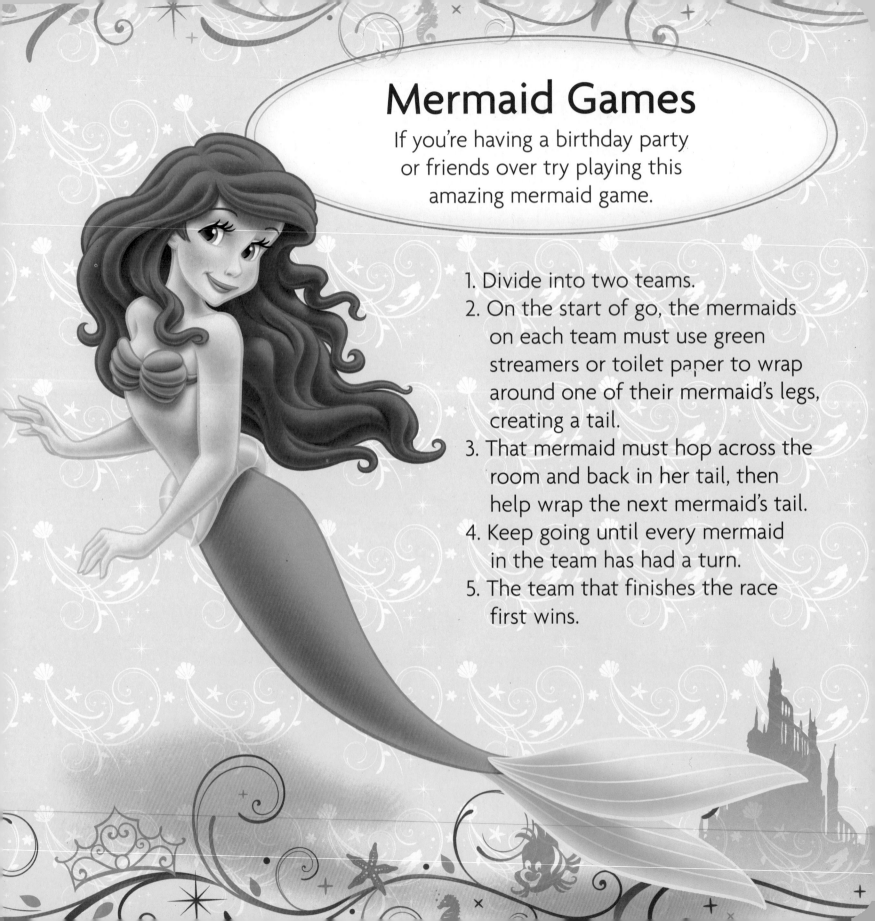

Mermaid Games

If you're having a birthday party or friends over try playing this amazing mermaid game.

1. Divide into two teams.
2. On the start of go, the mermaids on each team must use green streamers or toilet paper to wrap around one of their mermaid's legs, creating a tail.
3. That mermaid must hop across the room and back in her tail, then help wrap the next mermaid's tail.
4. Keep going until every mermaid in the team has had a turn.
5. The team that finishes the race first wins.

Three in a Row

1. Find a friend.
2. Decide which of you will be Flounder and which of you will be Sebastian.
3. Take it in turns to write F and S in the grid.
4. The winner is the first person to get three in a row.

Answer:

Look and Find

Ursula is an evil sea witch. She is hiding somewhere in this picture. Can you spot her?

My Mermaid

Ever wondered what you would look like if you were a mermaid? Draw yourself as a mermaid here.

Odd One Out

Ariel has fallen in love with Prince Eric. Which one is the real Eric? *Hint: he is different to all the others.*

Answer:

Wordsearch

Ariel is collecting pearls for a necklace. How many times can you find the word pearl in this wordsearch? Circle the words when you find them.

Tip: *Look down and across!*

P	E	A	R	L	L	X	P	Z
E	K	I	V	T	Y	E	U	U
A	D	G	U	S	J	A	M	M
R	F	T	P	E	A	R	L	L
L	S	W	E	O	X	L	Y	Y
B	F	C	A	T	H	Q	U	U
D	N	U	R	Z	I	O	B	B
Z	X	C	L	S	L	K	D	D

Answer: 5

Colour by Numbers

Ariel's father, King Triton, is really protective of Ariel.
Follow the colour code to complete this picture.

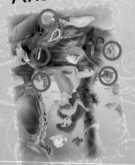

Underwater Treasures

Ariel and her best friend, Flounder, love to explore for treasure. Find five differences between these two pictures.

Flounder Fun

Use the top grid as a guide to draw Ariel's favourite fish friend in the bottom grid.

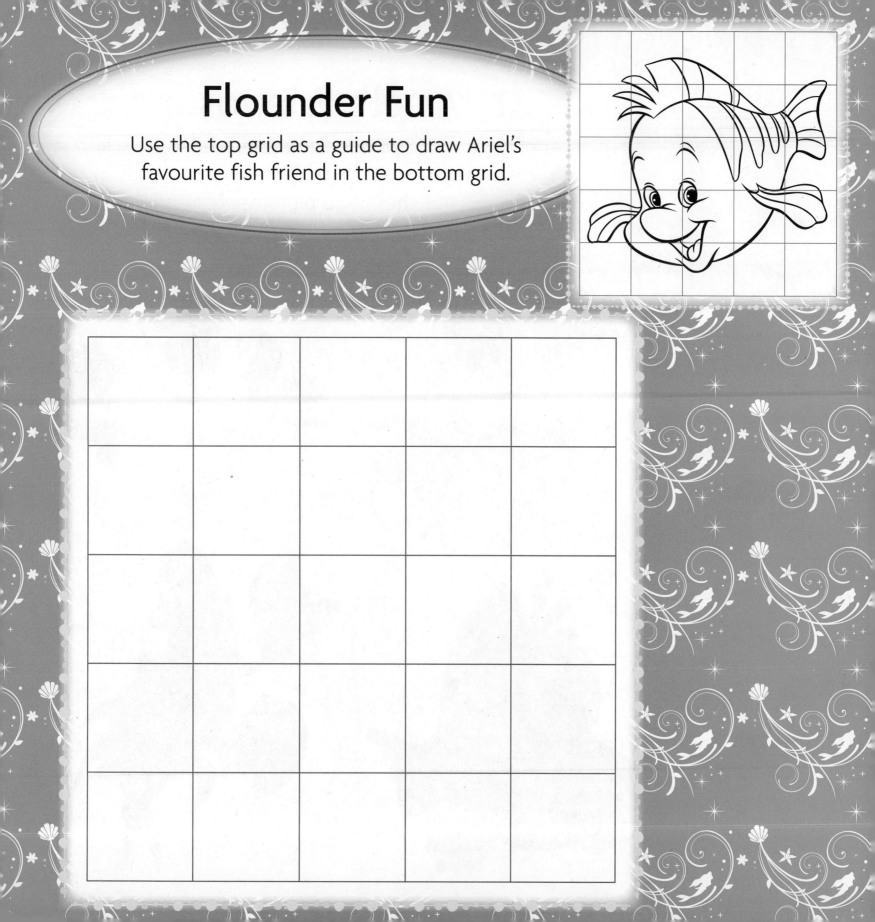

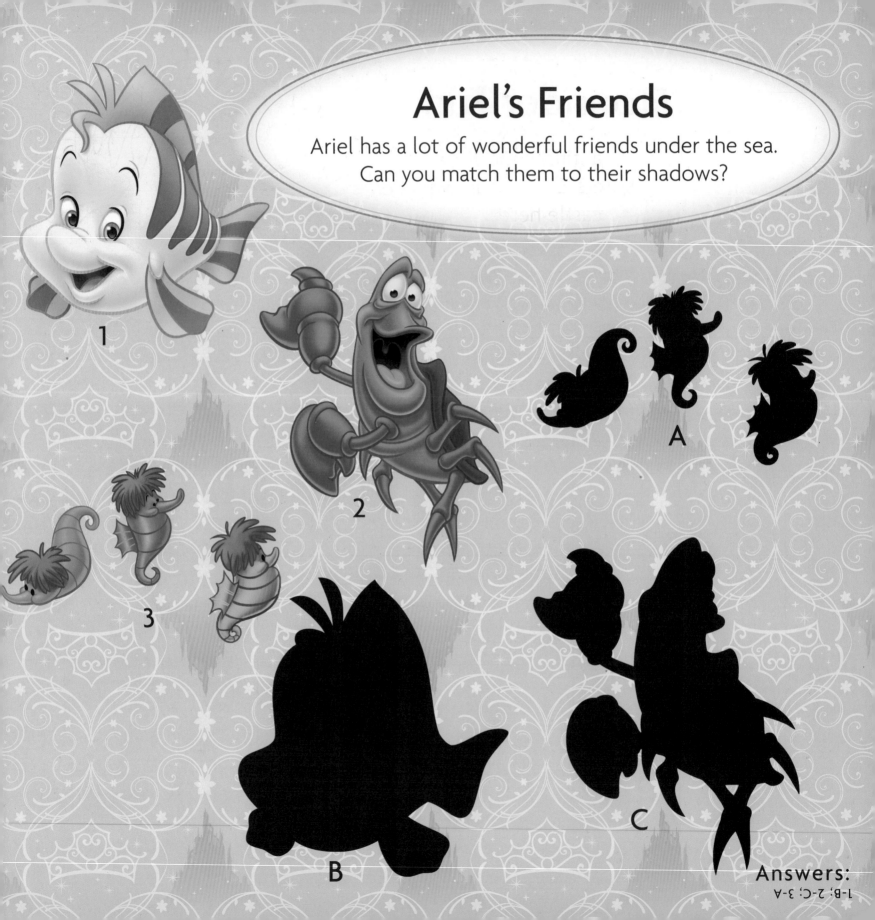

Ariel's Friends

Ariel has a lot of wonderful friends under the sea.
Can you match them to their shadows?

1

2

3

A

B

C

Enchanted Ocean

Ariel lives in a beautiful underwater home with her father and sisters. Draw your own underwater castle here....

Will it have a tall tower?

How many windows will it have?

What colour will it be?